A LITTLE SPOT IN A WORLD OF WORDS

ONE WAY

Be Kind

To my children, Ryan and Anna, who always ask me, "Why do I have to read so much?"

WE ARE HAVING A SALE

Be Kind

IMPORTANT NOTICE

You're invited to a Party!

Hi, how are you?

Just to let you know...

Dear Grandma,

Words can even help you understand what you are watching, even if you don't have sound! By reading subtitles, you can watch your favorite video that's in a different language.

So many feelings that can be found

When you are out and about, you will see words all around you. Reading signs will help you get to where you are going, so you don't get lost and stay safe.

People love to communicate through writing emails, text messages, and letters in the mail. You could read that you've been invited to a party in three different ways!

You can find words in math, too!
You need to be able to read instructions
and word problems!

I would have 13 cats!
That would be amazing!

Addition

MATH

Word Problem

Anna has 10 cats and gets 3 more. How many cats does she have?

Any time you see words around you, try and read them! The more you practice reading the better you will get! See you next time to learn something new!

Author's Note

I wrote this book when I found out that only 40% of the population in the United States can read over a 4th-grade reading level, and 20% of adults can't read at all. When I started to dig further into our literacy rate, I also discovered that dyslexia is not recognized as a disability in many states around the country. When dyslexia is recognized as a learning disability in the state, teachers are rarely shown how to identify it in their students.

More awareness is needed to help our literacy crisis, and we desperately need to help our children read. I created this reading series in hopes of making reading fun and to open a dialogue between you and your child. I encourage you to ask them questions as you read this book. We can all agree that English is a very complex language to learn, and our children could use all the help they can get.

-Diane Alber

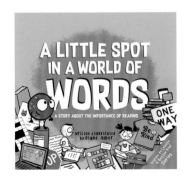

How many of these **A Little SPOT books** have you read?

A Little SPOT of Emotion Box Set

- ☐ A Little SPOT of Anger
- ☐ A Little SPOT of Anxiety
- ☐ A Little SPOT of Happiness
- ☐ A Little SPOT of Sadness
- ☐ A Little SPOT of Love
- ☐ A Little SPOT of Confidence
- ☐ A Little Peaceful SPOT
- ☐ A Little Scribble SPOT

A Little SPOT of Feelings Box Set

- ☐ A Little SPOT of Empathy
- ☐ A Little SPOT of Frustration
- ☐ A Little Calm SPOT
- ☐ A Little SPOT of Worry
- ☐ A Little SPOT of Belonging
- ☐ A Little SPOT of Flexible Thinking
- ☐ A Little SPOT of Boredom
- ☐ A Little SPOT of Feelings: Emotion Detective

A Little SPOT of Life Skills Box Set

- ☐ A Little SPOT of Courage
- ☐ A Little SPOT of Perseverance
- ☐ A Little SPOT of Teamwork
- ☐ A Little SPOT of Talent
- ☐ A Little Thankful SPOT
- ☐ A Little SPOT of Giving
- ☐ A Little SPOT of Optimism
- ☐ A Little SPOT of Creativity

A Little SPOT Takes Action Box Set

- ☐ A Little SPOT of Kindness
- ☐ A Little SPOT of Patience
- ☐ A Little SPOT of Responsibility
- ☐ A Little SPOT of Organization
- ☐ A Little Respectful SPOT
- ☐ A Little SPOT of Honesty
- ☐ A Little Safety SPOT
- ☐ Finding Your SPOT In The World

Wellness Books

- ☐ A Little Sleepy SPOT

Learning Books

- ☐ A Little SPOT Learns Letters
- ☐ A little SPOT Lives in a World of Words
- ☐ A Little SPOT Learns to Read
- ☐ A Little SPOT Learns Online

Holiday Books

- ☐ A Little SPOT of Thanksgiving
- ☐ A Little SPOT of Christmas